Maths
made easy

Key Stage 2
ages 8–9
Advanced

Author and Consultant
Sean McArdle

LONDON • NEW YORK • MUNICH • MELBOURNE • DELHI

Adding and subtracting

Add 100 to 356.

456

Add 1 000 to 2 376.

3 376

Subtract 100 from 5 324.

5 224

Subtract 1 000 from 7 296.

6 296

Add 100 to each number.

376		795		646		585	
286		57		4 312		5 634	
12		4 789		924		3 903	

Add 1 000 to each number.

485		607		37		943	
3 587		7 056		5 045		2 907	
5 897		9 564		5 499		9 001	

Subtract 100 from each number.

364		729		477		765	
103		146		1 003		599	
100		5 745		3 078		6 107	

Subtract 1 000 from each number.

4 734		8 610		5 307		9 362	
12 675		4 907		8 445		1 001	
1 400		15 638		20 832		14 056	

Dividing by 10 and 100

Divide 90 by 10.

Divide 3 400 by 100.

9

34

Divide each number by 10.

60		80		10		50	
100		150		230		300	
210		170		20		260	
40		360		590		730	
420		380		820		540	

Divide each number by 100.

300		700		900		100	
600		800		1 100		1 400	
1 700		1 900		2 300		2 800	
3 800		4 100		8 400		9 400	
6 000		1 000		7 500		5 600	

Divide each number by 10.

700		2 300		4 100		3 650	
6 480		7 080		3 540		2 030	
1 030		9 670		6 320		1 400	
300		900		1 020		3 660	
20		18 000		13 600		17 890	

Negative numbers

ARTHUR, Jan 2014.

This is the temperature outside at midnight.

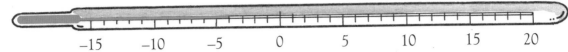

The temperature rises by 12°C by midday. What is the temperature at midday?   8°C

The temperature on each of these thermometers rises by 8°C. What is the new temperature each time?

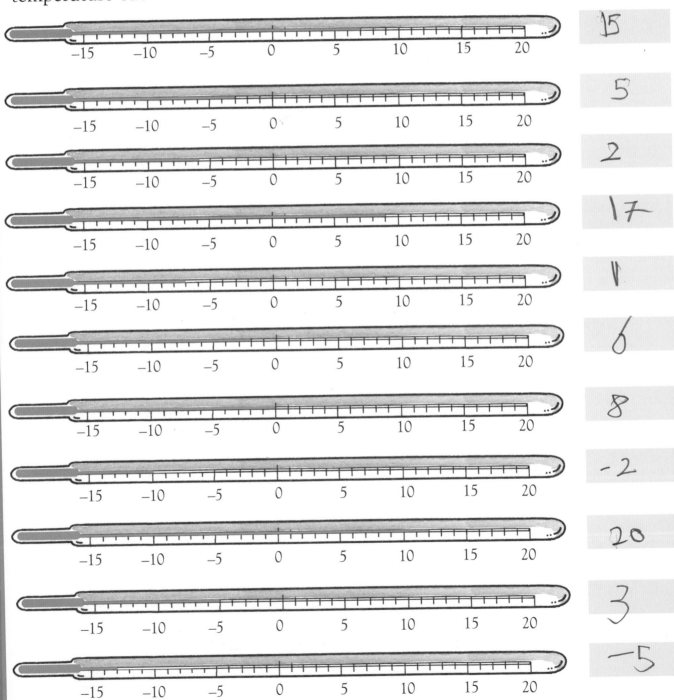

15

5

2

17

1

6

8

- 2

20

3

-5

Counting in steps

Continue each sequence.

| 11 | 22 | 33 | 44 | 55 | 66 | 77 | 88 |
| 12 | 24 | 36 | 48 | 60 | 72 | 84 | 96 |

Continue each sequence.

12	23	34	45	56			
9	21	33	45	57			
32	43	54	65	76			
2	14	26	38	50			
−20	−9	2	13	24			
−30	−18	−6	6	18			
−41	−30	−19	−8	3			
−60	−48	−36	−24	−12			

Continue each sequence.

45	34	23	12	1			
70	58	46	34	22			
44	33	22	11	0			
48	36	24	12	0			
7	−4	−15	−26	−37			
14	2	−10	−22	−34			
8	−3	−14	−25	−36			
10	−2	−14	−26	−38			

Multiples

Circle the multiples of 11.

| 9 | 16 | (22) | 34 | (44) | 60 | (77) | 90 |

Circle the multiples of 12.

| 14 | 26 | 39 | (48) | 63 | (72) | 94 | 100 |

Circle the multiples of 11.

1	7	11	18	24	32	44	58
6	13	22	34	44	54	66	77
11	14	21	26	55	88	99	100
20	25	30	35	40	45	50	55
66	26	46	64	44	24	62	72
16	24	32	40	48	56	64	72
11	22	33	44	55	66	78	88
96	73	11	45	62	77	14	33

Circle the multiples of 12.

4	8	12	16	20	24	28	32
9	12	15	18	21	24	27	30
6	12	18	24	30	36	42	48
8	16	24	32	40	48	56	64
9	18	27	36	45	54	63	72
10	20	30	40	50	60	70	80
12	24	36	48	60	72	84	96
68	56	44	32	20	12	0	36

Square numbers

The square has two rows and two columns. It is 2^2.

How many dots are there?   4

2^2 is the same as
$2 \times 2 = 4$

Draw a picture like the one above to show each of these numbers.

3^2

How many
dots are there?

4^2

How many
dots are there?

5^2

How many
dots are there?

6^2

How many
dots are there?

7^2

How many
dots are there?

8^2

How many
dots are there?

9^2

How many dots are there?

10^2

How many dots are there?

Fractions and decimals

Write each fraction as a decimal.

$\frac{1}{2}$ = 0.5 $\frac{1}{10}$ = 0.1

Write this decimal as a fraction.

0.25 = $\frac{1}{4}$

Write each fraction as a decimal.

$\frac{1}{4}$		$\frac{1}{2}$		$\frac{3}{4}$		$\frac{1}{5}$	
$\frac{2}{5}$		$\frac{3}{5}$		$\frac{4}{5}$		$\frac{1}{10}$	
$\frac{2}{10}$		$\frac{3}{10}$		$\frac{4}{10}$		$\frac{5}{10}$	
$\frac{6}{10}$		$\frac{7}{10}$		$\frac{8}{10}$		$\frac{9}{10}$	

Write each decimal as a fraction.

0.8		0.5		0.3		0.4	
0.25		0.7		0.2		0.75	
0.2		0.6		0.5		0.8	
0.1		0.4		0.6		0.9	

Write the answer in the box.

Which two of the fractions above are the same as 0.5?

Which two of the fractions above are the same as 0.8?

Which two of the fractions above are the same as 0.6?

Which two of the fractions above are the same as 0.2?

Which two of the fractions above are the same as 0.4?

Fractions of shapes

Shade $\frac{3}{5}$ of each shape.

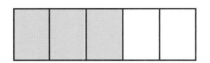
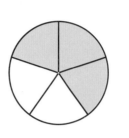

Shade $\frac{4}{5}$ of each shape.

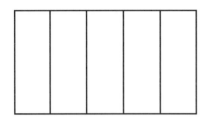
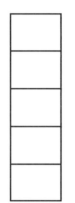

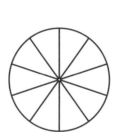
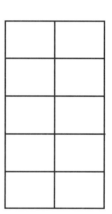

Shade the amount shown of each shape.

Two-fifths

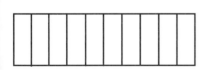

Four-fifths

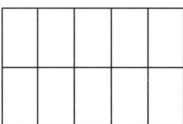

Three-tenths

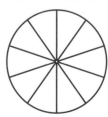

Seven-tenths

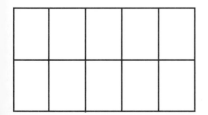

Three-fifths

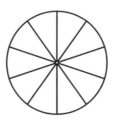

Nine-tenths

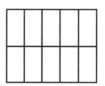

Ordering decimals

Write each row in order starting with the smallest.

| 1.7 m | 1.3 m | 1.5 m | 1.9 m | 1.3 m | 1.5 m | 1.7 m | 1.9 m |
| 5.3 m | 2.8 m | 3.9 m | 1.6 m | 1.6 m | 2.8 m | 3.9 m | 5.3 m |

Write each row in order starting with the smallest.

2.4 m	2.8 m	2.1 m	2.6 m	2.9 m					
5.2 m	5.7 m	5.1 m	5.8 m	5.3 m					
1.4 m	1.7 m	1.8 m	1.1 m	1.9 m					
3.8 m	3.6 m	3.4 m	3.2 m	3.1 m					
7.5 m	7.3 m	7.9 m	7.2 m	7.8 m					
4.3 m	4.6 m	4.0 m	4.2 m	4.8 m					
6.9 m	6.0 m	6.4 m	6.2 m	6.7 m					
10.6 m	10.3 m	10.8 m	10.5 m	10.0 m					
7.4 m	6.4 m	9.4 m	2.4 m	8.4 m					
3.7 m	6.7 m	7.7 m	2.7 m	9.7 m					
4.5 m	1.5 m	3.5 m	8.5 m	10.5 m					
6.9 m	1.9 m	8.9 m	9.9 m	5.9 m					
0.6 m	2.6 m	1.6 m	6.6 m	9.6 m					
3.5 m	1.8 m	2.7 m	4.3 m	7.9 m					
7.6 m	2.3 m	4.9 m	1.6 m	0.3 m					
2.0 m	0.7 m	3.5 m	8.1 m	4.6 m					

Rounding decimals

Write each amount to the nearest pound.

£1.67	£2.83	£1.23	£3.28
£2.00	£3.00	£1.00	£3.00

Write each amount to the nearest pound.

£2.67		£3.18		£6.75		£7.43	
£8.28		£8.67		£4.97		£2.43	
£4.66		£8.12		£6.08		£5.40	
£7.02		£6.74		£7.83		£12.78	
£11.64		£10.64		£15.67		£21.37	

Write each length to the nearest metre.

1.76 m		4.32 m		6.75 m		3.84 m	
7.40 m		3.18 m		7.31 m		9.63 m	
5.42 m		12.82 m		18.53 m		16.45 m	
10.53 m		20.65 m		17.45 m		14.32 m	
12.64 m		19.05 m		15.51 m		27.47 m	

Write each amount to the nearest pound or metre.

3.46 m		£2.50		4.50 m		£7.50	
12.50 m		18.99 m		£12.50		23.50 m	
35.50 m		£61.67		50.50 m		67.50 m	
£45.67		£63.50		£89.78		34.50 m	
£58.50		£21.56		£95.50		64.50 m	

Adding – Two stage method

Write the answer in the box

67 + 32   39 + 43   45 + 26

67 + 30 = 97   39 + 40 = 79   45 + 20 = 65
97 + 2 = 99   79 + 3 = 82   65 + 6 = 71

Work out each addition using the same method.

43 + 25	72 + 16	56 + 14	28 + 15	47 + 13
36 + 15	54 + 17	84 + 13	47 + 16	54 + 19
45 + 15	48 + 14	64 + 19	70 + 14	45 + 17
18 + 33	17 + 44	14 + 56	18 + 44	14 + 44
26 + 36	45 + 34	74 + 18	36 + 17	81 + 8
45 + 35	43 + 28	57 + 44	49 + 37	37 + 46

Adding – Two stage method

Write the answer in the box

35m + 27m   74km + 18km   46g + 38g

35 + 20 = 55m   74 + 10 = 84km   46 + 30 = 76g
55 + 7 = 62m   84 + 8 = 92km   76 + 8 = 84g

Work out each addition using the same method.

37m + 46m   56m + 36m   68m + 45m   49m + 27m
_____   _____   _____   _____

47km + 44km   29km + 34km   56km + 35km   55km + 37km
_____   _____   _____   _____

65kg + 27kg   43kg + 18kg   52kg + 17kg   47kg + 27kg
_____   _____   _____   _____

57g + 42g   48g + 24g   44g + 18g   66g + 27g
_____   _____   _____   _____

£23.00 + £18.00   £36.00 + £43.00   £75.00 + £16.00   £27.00 + £38.00
_____   _____   _____   _____

Adding

Write the answer between the lines.

$35 + 17 + 16$ $38 + 24 + 17$ $24 + 16 + 19$

$30 + 10 + 10 = 50$ $30 + 20 + 10 = 60$ $20 + 10 + 10 = 40$
$5 + 7 + 6 = 18$ $8 + 4 + 7 = 19$ $4 + 6 + 9 = 19$

68   79   59

Work out each addition using the same method.

$12 + 13 + 13$ $17 + 10 + 11$ $15 + 13 + 11$ $12 + 14 + 12$

$17 + 26 + 12$ $19 + 13 + 14$ $16 + 21 + 31$ $12 + 25 + 33$

$20 + 32 + 16$ $30 + 26 + 25$ $40 + 42 + 25$ $50 + 21 + 21$

$25 + 15 + 5$ $35 + 25 + 5$ $45 + 15 + 5$ $55 + 35 + 5$

$23 + 45 + 32$ $34 + 32 + 13$ $45 + 16 + 9$ $56 + 16 + 7$

Subtracting

Write the answer between the lines.

57	42	36
− 15	− 16	− 29
42	26	7

Write the answer between the lines.

40	60	70	50	90
− 18	− 23	− 37	− 18	− 27

41	62	85	64	71
− 14	− 15	− 37	− 45	− 36

45	65	75	95	85
− 18	− 34	− 69	− 49	− 38

73	82	74	81	64
− 27	− 38	− 47	− 39	− 47

61	52	61	53	73
− 14	− 17	− 19	− 23	− 44

70	63	83	53	47
− 26	− 7	− 56	− 36	− 43

Subtracting

Write the answer between the lines.

56 m	37 km	58 kg
− 18 m	− 19 km	− 19 kg
38 m	18 km	39 kg

Write the answer between the lines.

45 m	63 m	74 m	82 m	40 m
− 23 m	− 44 m	− 38 m	− 29 m	− 17 m

61 m	81 m	62 m	83 m	43 m
− 27 m	− 36 m	− 27 m	− 36 m	− 17 m

45 m	60 m	73 m	74 m	85 m
− 26 m	− 47 m	− 48 m	− 39 m	− 47 m

Write the answer between the lines.

50 km	37 km	75 km	84 km	90 km
− 28 km	− 18 km	− 39 km	− 29 km	− 37 km

Write the answer between the lines.

68 kg	47 kg	64 kg	79 kg	56 kg
− 39 kg	− 38 kg	− 27 kg	− 27 kg	− 45 kg

Answer Section with Parents' Notes
Key Stage 2
Ages 8–9
Advanced

This 8-page section provides answers to all the activities in this book. This will enable you to mark your children's work or can be used by them if they prefer to do their own marking.

The notes for each page help explain the common pitfalls and problems and, where appropriate, give indications as to what practice is needed to ensure your children understand where they have gone wrong.

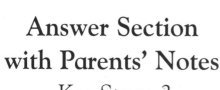

Adding and subtracting

Add 100 to 356.	Add 1 000 to 2 376.
456	3 376
Subtract 100 from 5 324.	Subtract 1 000 from 7 296.
5224	6296

Add 100 to each number.

376	476	795	895	646	746	585	685
286	386	57	157	4312	4412	5634	5734
12	112	4789	4889	924	1024	3903	4003

Add 1 000 to each number.

485	1485	607	1607	37	1037	943	1943
3587	4587	7056	8056	5045	6045	2907	3907
5897	6897	9564	10564	5499	6499	9001	10001

Subtract 100 from each number.

364	264	729	629	477	377	765	665
103	3	146	46	1003	903	599	499
100	0	5745	5645	3078	2978	6107	6007

Subtract 1 000 from each number.

4734	3734	8610	7610	5307	4307	9362	8362
12675	11675	4907	3907	8445	7445	1001	1
1400	400	15638	14638	20832	19832	14056	13056

Children should be aware that adding 100 will increase the digit in the hundreds column by 1 and may also have an effect on the thousands column. This also applies to the process of adding 1 000, and the opposite when subtracting 100 or 1 000.

Dividing by 10 and 100

Divide 90 by 10.	Divide 3 400 by 100.
9	34

Divide each number by 10.

60	6	80	8	10	1	50	5
100	10	150	15	230	23	300	30
210	21	170	17	20	2	260	26
40	4	360	36	590	59	730	73
420	42	380	38	820	82	540	54

Divide each number by 100.

300	3	700	7	900	9	100	1
600	6	800	8	1 100	11	1 400	14
1 700	17	1 900	19	2 300	23	2 800	28
3 800	38	4 100	41	8 400	84	9 400	94
6 000	60	1 000	10	7 500	75	5 600	56

Divide each number by 10.

700	70	2 300	230	4 100	410	3 650	365
6480	648	7 080	708	3 540	354	2 030	203
1 030	103	9 670	967	6 320	632	1 400	140
300	30	900	90	1 020	102	3 660	366
20	2	18 000	1800	13 600	1360	17 890	1789

Many children will give correct answers because they quickly realise that it is just a matter of 'taking off a nought'. They should also realise that this happens because they are finding how many lots of 10 there are in the number given.

Negative numbers

This is the temperature outside at midnight.

The temperature rises by 12°C by midday. What is the temperature at midday? 8°C

The temperature on each of these thermometers rises by 8°C. What is the new temperature each time?

15°C
5°C
2°C
17°C
1°C
6°C
8°C
−2°C
20°C
3°C
−5°C

At this stage children should understand the word 'rises' in the question and its significance. Though the children may refer to the thermometers, ask them to try to work out one of the answers in their heads to see if they can visualise the problem properly.

Counting in steps

Continue each sequence.

| 11 | 22 | 33 | 44 | 55 | **66** | **77** | **88** |
| 12 | 24 | 36 | 48 | 60 | **72** | **84** | **96** |

Continue each sequence.

12	23	34	45	56	**67**	**78**	**89**
9	21	33	45	57	**69**	**81**	**93**
32	43	54	65	76	**87**	**98**	**109**
2	14	26	38	50	**62**	**74**	**86**
−20	−9	2	13	24	**35**	**46**	**57**
−30	−18	−6	6	18	**30**	**42**	**54**
−41	−30	−19	−8	3	**14**	**25**	**36**
−60	−48	−36	−24	−12	**0**	**12**	**24**

Continue each sequence.

45	34	23	12	1	**−10**	**−21**	**−32**
70	58	46	34	22	**10**	**−2**	**−14**
44	33	22	11	0	**−11**	**−22**	**−33**
48	36	24	12	0	**−12**	**−24**	**−36**
7	−4	−15	−26	−37	**−48**	**−59**	**−70**
14	2	−10	−22	−34	**−46**	**−58**	**−70**
8	−3	−14	−25	−36	**−47**	**−58**	**−69**
10	−2	−14	−26	−38	**−50**	**−62**	**−74**

The questions that cross the zero boundary are most likely to cause problems. Watch out for the 8th sequence. Any mistakes may be remedied by drawing a simple number line, such as that used on the thermometer on the previous page.

Multiples

Circle the multiples of 11.

| 9 | 16 | (22) | 34 | (44) | 60 | (77) | 90 |

Circle the multiples of 12.

| 14 | 26 | 39 | (48) | 63 | (72) | 94 | 100 |

Circle the multiples of 11.

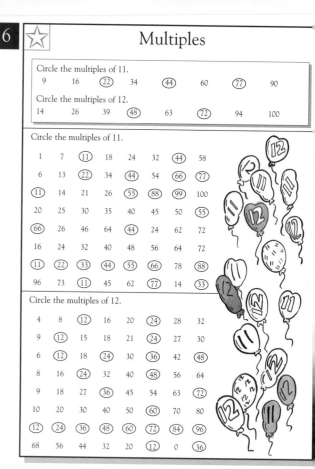

1	7	(11)	18	24	32	(44)	58
6	13	(22)	34	(44)	54	(66)	(77)
(11)	14	21	26	(55)	(88)	(99)	100
20	25	30	35	40	45	50	(55)
(66)	26	46	64	(44)	24	62	72
16	24	32	40	48	56	64	72
(11)	(22)	(33)	(44)	(55)	(66)	78	(88)
96	73	(11)	45	62	(77)	14	(33)

Circle the multiples of 12.

4	8	(12)	16	20	(24)	28	32
9	(12)	15	18	21	(24)	27	30
6	(12)	18	(24)	30	(36)	42	(48)
8	16	(24)	32	40	(48)	56	64
9	18	27	(36)	45	54	63	(72)
10	20	30	40	50	(60)	70	80
(12)	(24)	(36)	(48)	(60)	(72)	(84)	(96)
68	56	44	32	20	(12)	0	(36)

The children should spot the multiples of 11 fairly easily but in the 7th row they might be careless wit 78. The multiples of 12 are not so easy to spot and may be worthwhile seeing if the children can exten beyond the ones in the 7th row.

Square numbers

The square has two rows and two columns. It is 2^2.
How many dots are there? **4**
2^2 is the same as $2 \times 2 = 4$

Draw a picture like the one above to show each of these numbers squared.

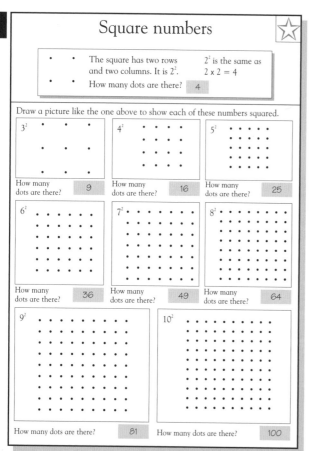

3^2 How many dots are there? **9**

4^2 How many dots are there? **16**

5^2 How many dots are there? **25**

6^2 How many dots are there? **36**

7^2 How many dots are there? **49**

8^2 How many dots are there? **64**

9^2 How many dots are there? **81**

10^2 How many dots are there? **100**

This is a traditional way of showing square numbers but many children will pick up the idea of 'multiplying the number by itself' fairly quickly. If the children pick up the idea do not make them draw the dots but talk through the work with them instead.

Fractions and decimals

Write each fraction as a decimal.

$\frac{1}{2}$ = **0.5** $\frac{1}{10}$ = **0.1**

Write this decimal as a fraction.

0.25 = **$\frac{1}{4}$**

Write each fraction as a decimal.

$\frac{1}{4}$	**0.25**	$\frac{1}{2}$	**0.5**	$\frac{3}{4}$	**0.75**	$\frac{1}{5}$	**0.2**
$\frac{2}{5}$	**0.4**	$\frac{3}{5}$	**0.6**	$\frac{4}{5}$	**0.8**	$\frac{1}{10}$	**0.1**
$\frac{2}{10}$	**0.2**	$\frac{3}{10}$	**0.3**	$\frac{4}{10}$	**0.4**	$\frac{5}{10}$	**0.5**
$\frac{6}{10}$	**0.6**	$\frac{7}{10}$	**0.7**	$\frac{8}{10}$	**0.8**	$\frac{9}{10}$	**0.9**

Write each decimal as a fraction.

0.8	**$\frac{8}{10}$**	0.5	**$\frac{5}{10}$**	0.3	**$\frac{3}{10}$**	0.4	**$\frac{2}{5}$**
0.25	**$\frac{1}{4}$**	0.7	**$\frac{7}{10}$**	0.2	**$\frac{1}{5}$**	0.75	**$\frac{3}{4}$**
0.2	**$\frac{2}{10}$**	0.6	**$\frac{6}{10}$**	0.5	**$\frac{1}{2}$**	0.8	**$\frac{4}{5}$**
0.1	**$\frac{1}{10}$**	0.4	**$\frac{4}{10}$**	0.6	**$\frac{3}{5}$**	0.9	**$\frac{9}{10}$**

Write the answer in the box.

Which two of the fractions above are the same as 0.5? **$\frac{5}{10}$ $\frac{1}{2}$**

Which two of the fractions above are the same as 0.8? **$\frac{8}{10}$ $\frac{4}{5}$**

Which two of the fractions above are the same as 0.6? **$\frac{6}{10}$ $\frac{3}{5}$**

Which two of the fractions above are the same as 0.2? **$\frac{1}{5}$ $\frac{2}{10}$**

Which two of the fractions above are the same as 0.4? **$\frac{4}{10}$ $\frac{2}{5}$**

In the 3rd section children are asked to give the sam decimal in two different ways and they may choose t write either one first. They may not have been told about equivalent fractions, which is what many of these are. This may therefore be worth a discussion.

9 — Fractions of shapes ☆

Shade $\frac{3}{5}$ of each shape.

Shade $\frac{4}{5}$ of each shape.

Shade the amount shown of each shape.

Two-fifths   Four-fifths   Three-tenths

Seven-tenths   Three-fifths   Nine-tenths

Knowledge of equivalence of fractions is being tested in some of these questions although the children may not know it by that name. For example, when $\frac{4}{5}$ of ten sections needs to be shaded, does the child recognise that $\frac{4}{5}$ of 10 is 8?

10 ☆ — Ordering decimals

Write each row in order starting with the smallest.

| 1.7 m | 1.3 m | 1.5 m | 1.9 m | 1.3 m | 1.5 m | 1.7 m | 1.9 m |
| 5.3 m | 2.8 m | 3.9 m | 1.6 m | 1.6 m | 2.8 m | 3.9 m | 5.3 m |

Write each row in order starting with the smallest.

2.4 m	2.8 m	2.1 m	2.6 m	2.9 m	2.1 m	2.4 m	2.6 m	2.8 m	2.9 m
5.2 m	5.7 m	5.1 m	5.8 m	5.3 m	5.1 m	5.2 m	5.3 m	5.7 m	5.8 m
1.4 m	1.7 m	1.8 m	1.1 m	1.9 m	1.1 m	1.4 m	1.7 m	1.8 m	1.9 m
3.8 m	3.6 m	3.4 m	3.2 m	3.1 m	3.1 m	3.2 m	3.4 m	3.6 m	3.8 m
7.5 m	7.3 m	7.9 m	7.2 m	7.8 m	7.2 m	7.3 m	7.5 m	7.8 m	7.9 m
4.3 m	4.6 m	4.0 m	4.2 m	4.8 m	4.0 m	4.2 m	4.3 m	4.6 m	4.8 m
6.9 m	6.0 m	6.4 m	6.2 m	6.7 m	6.0 m	6.2 m	6.4 m	6.7 m	6.9 m
10.6 m	10.3 m	10.8 m	10.5 m	10.0 m	10.0 m	10.3 m	10.5 m	10.6 m	10.8 m
7.4 m	6.4 m	9.4 m	2.4 m	8.4 m	2.4 m	6.4 m	7.4 m	8.4 m	9.4 m
3.7 m	6.7 m	7.7 m	2.7 m	9.7 m	2.7 m	3.7 m	6.7 m	7.7 m	9.7 m
4.5 m	1.5 m	3.5 m	8.5 m	10.5 m	1.5 m	3.5 m	4.5 m	8.5 m	10.5 m
6.9 m	1.9 m	8.9 m	9.9 m	5.9 m	1.9 m	5.9 m	6.9 m	8.9 m	9.9 m
0.6 m	2.6 m	1.6 m	6.6 m	9.6 m	0.6 m	1.6 m	2.6 m	6.6 m	9.6 m
3.5 m	1.8 m	2.7 m	4.3 m	7.9 m	1.8 m	2.7 m	3.5 m	4.3 m	7.9 m
7.6 m	2.3 m	4.9 m	1.6 m	0.3 m	0.3 m	1.6 m	2.3 m	4.9 m	7.6 m
2.0 m	0.7 m	3.5 m	8.1 m	4.6 m	0.7 m	2.0 m	3.5 m	4.6 m	8.1 m

Children should successfully put the amounts in the first few examples in order as they all begin with the same number. In the later examples, they may need to be reminded that the digits in the tens/units columns must be dealt with before those in the first decimal place.

11 — Rounding decimals ☆

Write each amount to the nearest pound.

| £1.67 | £2.83 | £1.23 | £3.28 |
| £2.00 | £3.00 | £1.00 | £3.00 |

Write each amount to the nearest pound.

£2.67	£3.00	£3.18	£3.00	£6.75	£7.00	£7.43	£7.00
£8.28	£8.00	£8.67	£9.00	£4.97	£5.00	£2.43	£2.00
£4.66	£5.00	£8.12	£8.00	£6.08	£6.00	£5.40	£5.00
£7.02	£7.00	£6.74	£7.00	£7.83	£8.00	£12.78	£13.00
£11.64	£12.00	£10.64	£11.00	£15.67	£16.00	£21.37	£21.00

Write each length to the nearest metre.

1.76 m	2 m	4.32 m	4 m	6.75 m	7 m	3.84 m	4 m
7.40 m	7 m	3.18 m	3 m	7.31 m	7 m	9.63 m	10 m
5.42 m	5 m	12.82 m	13 m	18.53 m	19 m	16.45 m	16 m
10.53 m	11 m	20.65 m	21 m	17.45 m	17 m	14.32 m	14 m
12.64 m	13 m	19.05 m	19 m	15.51 m	16 m	27.47 m	27 m

Write each amount to the nearest pound or metre.

3.46 m	3 m	£2.50	£3.00	4.50 m	5 m	£7.50	£8.00
12.50 m	13 m	18.99 m	19 m	£12.50	£13.00	23.50 m	24 m
35.50 m	36 m	£61.67	£62.00	50.50 m	51 m	67.50 m	68 m
£45.67	£46.00	£63.50	£64.00	£89.78	£90.00	34.50 m	35 m
£58.50	£59.00	£21.56	£22.00	£95.50	£96.00	64.50 m	65 m

The children should recognise the importance of the 50p or 50 cm border when rounding either up or down. Some of the questions in the 3rd section are half way between whole units and children should know that the convention is to round up when this occurs.

12 ☆ — Adding – Two stage method

Write the answer in the box

67 + 32
67 + 30 = 97
97 + 2 = 99

39 + 43
39 + 40 = 79
79 + 3 = 82

45 + 26
45 + 20 = 65
65 + 6 = 71

Work out each addition using the same method.

43 + 25
43 + 20 = 63
63 + 5 = 68

72 + 16
72 + 10 = 82
82 + 6 = 88

56 + 14
56 + 10 = 66
66 + 4 = 70

28 + 15
28 + 10 = 38
38 + 5 = 43

47 + 13
47 + 10 = 57
57 + 3 = 60

36 + 15
36 + 10 = 46
46 + 5 = 51

54 + 17
54 + 10 = 64
64 + 7 = 71

84 + 13
84 + 10 = 94
94 + 3 = 97

47 + 16
47 + 10 = 57
57 + 6 = 63

54 + 19
54 + 10 = 64
64 + 9 = 73

45 + 15
45 + 10 = 55
55 + 5 = 60

48 + 14
48 + 10 = 58
58 + 4 = 62

64 + 19
64 + 10 = 74
74 + 9 = 83

70 + 14
70 + 10 = 80
80 + 4 = 84

45 + 17
45 + 10 = 55
55 + 7 = 62

18 + 33
18 + 30 = 48
48 + 3 = 51

17 + 44
17 + 40 = 57
57 + 4 = 61

14 + 56
14 + 50 = 64
64 + 6 = 70

18 + 44
18 + 40 = 58
58 + 4 = 62

14 + 44
14 + 40 = 54
54 + 4 = 58

26 + 36
26 + 30 = 56
56 + 6 = 62

45 + 34
45 + 30 = 75
75 + 4 = 79

74 + 18
74 + 10 = 84
84 + 8 = 92

36 + 17
36 + 10 = 46
46 + 7 = 53

81 + 8
81 + 0 = 81
81 + 8 = 89

45 + 35
45 + 30 = 75
75 + 5 = 80

43 + 28
43 + 20 = 63
63 + 8 = 71

57 + 44
57 + 40 = 97
97 + 4 = 101

49 + 37
49 + 30 = 79
79 + 7 = 86

37 + 46
37 + 40 = 77
77 + 6 = 83

This method is widely taught nowadays and is an alternative to the more traditional column method. The method is very good and children who are doing well should be encouraged to work mentally, perhaps using jottings as reminders as they go.

13 | Adding – Two stage method ⭐

Write the answer in the box

35m + 27m	74km + 18km	46g + 38g
35 + 20 = 55m	74 + 10 = 84km	46 + 30 = 76g
55 + 7 = 62m	84 + 8 = 92km	76 + 8 = 84g

Work out each addition using the same method.

37m + 46m	56m + 36m	68m + 45m	49m + 27m
37 + 40 = 77	56 + 30 = 86	68 + 40 = 108	49 + 20 = 69
77 + 6 = 83m	86 + 6 = 92m	108 + 5 = 113m	69 + 7 = 76m

47km + 44km	29km + 34km	56km + 35km	55km + 37km
47 + 40 = 87	29 + 30 = 59	56 + 30 = 86	55 + 30 = 85
87 + 4 = 91km	59 + 4 = 63km	86 + 5 = 91km	85 + 7 = 92km

65kg + 27kg	43kg + 18kg	52kg + 17kg	47kg + 27kg
65 + 20 = 85	43 + 10 = 53	52 + 10 = 62	47 + 20 = 67
85 + 7 = 92kg	53 + 8 = 61kg	62 + 7 = 69kg	67 + 7 = 74kg

57g + 42g	48g + 24g	44g + 18g	66g + 27g
57 + 40 = 97	48 + 20 = 68	44 + 10 = 54	66 + 20 = 86
97 + 2 = 99g	68 + 4 = 72g	54 + 8 = 62g	86 + 7 = 93g

£23.00 + £18.00	£36.00 + £43.00	£75.00 + £16.00	£27.00 + £38.00
23 + 10 = 33	36 + 40 = 76	75 + 10 = 85	27 + 30 = 57
33 + 8 = £41.00	76 + 3 = £79.00	85 + 6 = £91.00	57 + 8 = £65.00

This method usually works well but some children find it helpful to jot down the total at the end of the first stage. Make sure the child includes the unit on the final total.

---

14 | ⭐ Adding

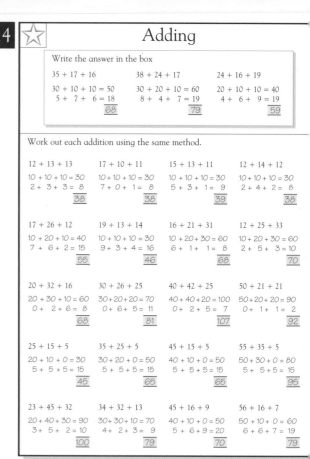

Write the answer in the box

35 + 17 + 16	38 + 24 + 17	24 + 16 + 19
30 + 10 + 10 = 50	30 + 20 + 10 = 60	20 + 10 + 10 = 40
5 + 7 + 6 = 18	8 + 4 + 7 = 19	4 + 6 + 9 = 19
68	79	59

Work out each addition using the same method.

12 + 13 + 13	17 + 10 + 11	15 + 13 + 11	12 + 14 + 12
10 + 10 + 10 = 30	10 + 10 + 10 = 30	10 + 10 + 10 = 30	10 + 10 + 10 = 30
2 + 3 + 3 = 8	7 + 0 + 1 = 8	5 + 3 + 1 = 9	2 + 4 + 2 = 8
38	38	39	38

17 + 26 + 12	19 + 13 + 14	16 + 21 + 31	12 + 25 + 33
10 + 20 + 10 = 40	10 + 10 + 10 = 30	10 + 20 + 30 = 60	10 + 20 + 30 = 60
7 + 6 + 2 = 15	9 + 3 + 4 = 16	6 + 1 + 1 = 8	2 + 5 + 3 = 10
55	46	68	70

20 + 32 + 16	30 + 26 + 25	40 + 42 + 25	50 + 21 + 21
20 + 30 + 10 = 60	30 + 20 + 20 = 70	40 + 40 + 20 = 100	50 + 20 + 20 = 90
0 + 2 + 6 = 8	0 + 6 + 5 = 11	0 + 2 + 5 = 7	0 + 1 + 1 = 2
68	81	107	92

25 + 15 + 5	35 + 25 + 5	45 + 15 + 5	55 + 35 + 5
20 + 10 + 0 = 30	30 + 20 + 0 = 50	40 + 10 + 0 = 50	50 + 30 + 0 = 80
5 + 5 + 5 = 15	5 + 5 + 5 = 15	5 + 5 + 5 = 15	5 + 5 + 5 = 15
45	65	65	95

23 + 45 + 32	34 + 32 + 13	45 + 16 + 9	56 + 16 + 7
20 + 40 + 30 = 90	30 + 30 + 10 = 70	40 + 10 + 0 = 50	50 + 10 + 0 = 60
3 + 5 + 2 = 10	4 + 2 + 3 = 9	5 + 6 + 9 = 20	6 + 6 + 7 = 19
100	79	70	79

This three stage method is widely used but with longer additions the child may find it helpful to keep notes at each stage. As the child becomes more confident have them try to work the answers mentally.

---

15 | Subtracting ⭐

Write the answer between the lines.

57	42	36
− 15	− 16	− 29
42	26	7

Write the answer between the lines.

40	60	70	50	90
− 18	− 23	− 37	− 18	− 27
22	37	33	32	63

41	62	85	64	71
− 14	− 15	− 37	− 45	− 36
27	47	48	19	35

45	65	75	95	85
− 18	− 34	− 69	− 49	− 38
27	31	6	46	47

73	82	74	81	64
− 27	− 38	− 47	− 39	− 47
46	44	27	42	17

61	52	61	53	73
− 14	− 17	− 19	− 23	− 44
47	35	42	30	29

70	63	83	53	47
− 26	− 7	− 56	− 36	− 43
44	56	27	17	4

Most of the subtraction sums require 'borrowing' or 'stealing' from the tens column, also known as 'exchanging'. Parents should talk through the methods of subtraction the children are using to make sure they are logical, accurate, and quick.

---

16 | ⭐ Subtracting

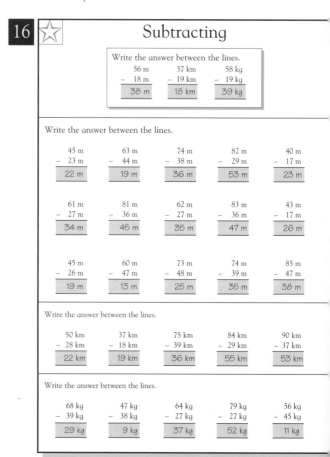

Write the answer between the lines.

56 m	37 km	58 kg
− 18 m	− 19 km	− 19 kg
38 m	18 km	39 kg

Write the answer between the lines.

45 m	63 m	74 m	82 m	40 m
− 23 m	− 44 m	− 38 m	− 29 m	− 17 m
22 m	19 m	36 m	53 m	23 m

61 m	81 m	62 m	83 m	43 m
− 27 m	− 36 m	− 27 m	− 36 m	− 17 m
34 m	45 m	35 m	47 m	26 m

45 m	60 m	73 m	74 m	85 m
− 26 m	− 47 m	− 48 m	− 39 m	− 47 m
19 m	13 m	25 m	35 m	38 m

Write the answer between the lines.

50 km	37 km	75 km	84 km	90 km
− 28 km	− 18 km	− 39 km	− 29 km	− 37 km
22 km	19 km	36 km	55 km	53 km

Write the answer between the lines.

68 kg	47 kg	64 kg	79 kg	56 kg
− 39 kg	− 38 kg	− 27 kg	− 27 kg	− 45 kg
29 kg	9 kg	37 kg	52 kg	11 kg

Children who are normally good at subtraction can be confused when there is a zero on the top line in the units column as, for example, with the 5th question. Any problems with these sums should be discussed.

Real life problems

Work out the sum and then write the answers.

Tuhil is reading a book that has 72 pages. He has read 38 pages. How many more pages does Tuhil have to read?

34 pages

$$\begin{array}{r} 72 \\ - 38 \\ \hline 34 \end{array}$$

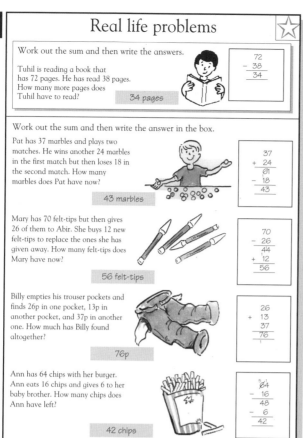

Work out the sum and then write the answer in the box.

Pat has 37 marbles and plays two matches. He wins another 24 marbles in the first match but then loses 18 in the second match. How many marbles does Pat have now?

43 marbles

$$\begin{array}{r} 37 \\ + 24 \\ \hline 61 \\ - 18 \\ \hline 43 \end{array}$$

Mary has 70 felt-tips but then gives 26 of them to Abir. She buys 12 new felt-tips to replace the ones she has given away. How many felt-tips does Mary have now?

56 felt-tips

$$\begin{array}{r} 70 \\ - 26 \\ \hline 44 \\ + 12 \\ \hline 56 \end{array}$$

Billy empties his trouser pockets and finds 26p in one pocket, 13p in another pocket, and 37p in another one. How much has Billy found altogether?

76p

$$\begin{array}{r} 26 \\ + 13 \\ 37 \\ \hline 76 \end{array}$$

Ann has 64 chips with her burger. Ann eats 16 chips and gives 6 to her baby brother. How many chips does Ann have left?

42 chips

$$\begin{array}{r} {}^{5}\cancel{6}4 \\ - 16 \\ \hline 48 \\ - 6 \\ \hline 42 \end{array}$$

Here the children work out which operation needs to be used. Although most children find simple symbolic problems like 12 + 16 easy, problems in a word context often confuse them. Parents should talk through any problems answered incorrectly.

Multiplying

Write the answer in the box

27 x 5	53 x 4	19 x 4
20 x 5 = 100	50 x 4 = 200	10 x 4 = 40
7 x 5 = 35	3 x 4 = 12	9 x 4 = 36
135	212	76

Write the answer between the lines.

26 x 4	43 x 4	67 x 4	18 x 4	74 x 4
20 x 4 = 80	40 x 4 = 160	60 x 4 = 240	10 x 4 = 40	70 x 4 = 280
6 x 4 = 24	3 x 4 = 12	7 x 4 = 28	8 x 4 = 32	4 x 4 = 16
104	172	268	72	296

19 x 3	41 x 3	58 x 3	32 x 3	94 x 3
10 x 3 = 30	40 x 3 = 120	50 x 3 = 150	30 x 3 = 90	90 x 3 = 270
9 x 3 = 27	1 x 3 = 3	8 x 3 = 24	2 x 3 = 6	4 x 3 = 12
57	123	174	96	282

33 x 5	49 x 5	67 x 5	28 x 5	63 x 5
30 x 5 = 150	40 x 5 = 200	60 x 5 = 300	20 x 5 = 100	60 x 5 = 300
3 x 5 = 15	9 x 5 = 45	7 x 5 = 35	8 x 5 = 40	3 x 5 = 15
165	245	335	140	315

64 x 2	85 x 2	94 x 2	57 x 2	78 x 2
60 x 2 = 120	80 x 2 = 160	90 x 2 = 180	50 x 2 = 100	70 x 2 = 140
4 x 2 = 8	5 x 2 = 10	4 x 2 = 8	7 x 2 = 14	8 x 2 = 16
128	170	188	114	156

15 x 6	53 x 6	64 x 6	85 x 6	72 x 6
10 x 6 = 60	50 x 6 = 300	60 x 6 = 360	80 x 6 = 480	70 x 6 = 420
5 x 6 = 30	3 x 6 = 18	4 x 6 = 24	5 x 6 = 30	2 x 6 = 12
90	318	384	510	432

37 x 8	85 x 8	51 x 8	84 x 8	47 x 8
30 x 8 = 240	80 x 8 = 640	50 x 8 = 400	80 x 8 = 640	40 x 8 = 320
7 x 8 = 56	5 x 8 = 40	1 x 8 = 8	4 x 8 = 32	7 x 8 = 56
296	680	408	672	376

Once the child is confident with this method they should be encouraged to leave pencil and paper methods, apart from jottings if needed. This method works very well mentally with even larger numbers.

Multiplying

Write the answer in the box

24 x 7	38 x 8	56 x 9
20 x 7 = 140	30 x 8 = 240	50 x 9 = 450
4 x 7 = 28	8 x 8 = 64	6 x 9 = 54
168	304	504

Write the answer between the lines.

43 x 7	50 x 7	37 x 7	29 x 7	16 x 7
40 x 7 = 280	50 x 7 = 350	30 x 7 = 210	20 x 7 = 140	10 x 7 = 70
3 x 7 = 21	0 x 7 = 0	7 x 7 = 49	9 x 7 = 63	6 x 7 = 42
301	350	259	203	112

27 x 9	58 x 9	36 x 9	14 x 9	61 x 9
20 x 9 = 180	50 x 9 = 450	30 x 9 = 270	10 x 9 = 90	60 x 9 = 540
7 x 9 = 63	8 x 9 = 72	6 x 9 = 54	4 x 9 = 36	1 x 9 = 9
243	522	324	126	549

53 x 10	37 x 10	49 x 10	58 x 10	67 x 10
50 x 10 = 500	30 x 10 = 300	40 x 10 = 400	50 x 10 = 500	60 x 10 = 600
3 x 10 = 30	7 x 10 = 70	9 x 10 = 90	8 x 10 = 80	7 x 10 = 70
530	370	490	580	670

37 x 4	47 x 5	87 x 6	17 x 7	97 x 8
30 x 4 = 120	40 x 5 = 200	80 x 6 = 480	10 x 7 = 70	90 x 8 = 720
7 x 4 = 28	7 x 5 = 35	7 x 6 = 42	7 x 7 = 49	7 x 8 = 56
148	235	522	119	776

58 x 6	38 x 7	78 x 8	28 x 9	18 x 10
50 x 6 = 300	30 x 7 = 210	70 x 8 = 560	20 x 9 = 180	10 x 10 = 100
8 x 6 = 48	8 x 7 = 56	8 x 8 = 64	8 x 9 = 72	8 x 10 = 80
348	266	624	252	180

49 x 5	29 x 6	59 x 7	89 x 8	69 x 9
40 x 5 = 200	20 x 6 = 120	50 x 7 = 350	80 x 8 = 640	60 x 9 = 540
9 x 5 = 45	9 x 6 = 54	9 x 7 = 63	9 x 8 = 72	9 x 9 = 81
245	174	413	712	621

This work covers the same method as the previous page but uses larger numbers. The child may need to make notes at each stage but this should become unnecessary as knowledge of times tables improves.

Dividing

Write the answer in the box.

24 ÷ 7 =	3 r 3		4 r 1	43 ÷ 8 =	5 r 3
		5 $\overline{)21}$			

Write the answer in the box.

27 ÷ 3 =	9	14 ÷ 3 =	4 r 2	23 ÷ 3 =	7 r 2
7 ÷ 3 =	2 r 1	31 ÷ 4 =	7 r 3	14 ÷ 4 =	3 r 2
38 ÷ 4 =	9 r 2	4 ÷ 4 =	1	42 ÷ 5 =	8 r 2
23 ÷ 5 =	4 r 3	15 ÷ 5 =	3	27 ÷ 5 =	5 r 2
47 ÷ 6 =	7 r 5	35 ÷ 5 =	7	46 ÷ 5 =	9 r 1
24 ÷ 5 =	4 r 4	42 ÷ 7 =	6	60 ÷ 7 =	8 r 4

Write the answer in the box.

4 r 2	5 r 6	2 r 5	7	3
8 $\overline{)34}$	8 $\overline{)46}$	8 $\overline{)21}$	8 $\overline{)56}$	9 $\overline{)27}$

5 r 1	6 r 4	8 r 2	7 r 1	10 r 1
9 $\overline{)46}$	9 $\overline{)58}$	9 $\overline{)74}$	2 $\overline{)15}$	2 $\overline{)21}$

1 r 1	8	5 r 2	7 r 2	10
2 $\overline{)3}$	2 $\overline{)16}$	3 $\overline{)17}$	3 $\overline{)23}$	3 $\overline{)30}$

8	3 r 1	6	7 r 3	10 r 3
3 $\overline{)24}$	4 $\overline{)13}$	4 $\overline{)24}$	4 $\overline{)31}$	4 $\overline{)43}$

Write the answer in the box.

45 ÷ 8 =	5 r 5	73 ÷ 8 =	9 r 1	56 ÷ 8 =	7
73 ÷ 9 =	8 r 1	41 ÷ 9 =	4 r 5	50 ÷ 9 =	5 r 5
54 ÷ 10 =	5 r 4	89 ÷ 10 =	8 r 9	42 ÷ 10 =	4 r 2

Children very often think that division sums are 'teacher's tricks' and are almost bound to have remainders to make them work harder! They seem puzzled by those that work out exactly.

21 Dividing

21

Write the answer in the box.

31 ÷ 4 = [7 r 3]   [2 r 5]   31 ÷ 9 = [3 r 4]
                   6)17

Write the answer in the box.

46 ÷ 9 = [5 r 1]	28 ÷ 7 = [4]	45 ÷ 9 = [5]
74 ÷ 8 = [9 r 2]	32 ÷ 3 = [10 r 2]	45 ÷ 7 = [6 r 3]
61 ÷ 7 = [8 r 5]	65 ÷ 9 = [7 r 2]	12 ÷ 9 = [1 r 3]
17 ÷ 4 = [4 r 1]	24 ÷ 6 = [4]	36 ÷ 6 = [6]
37 ÷ 8 = [4 r 5]	37 ÷ 9 = [4 r 1]	37 ÷ 10 = [3 r 7]
37 ÷ 6 = [6 r 1]	54 ÷ 6 = [9]	54 ÷ 7 = [7 r 5]

Write the answer in the box.

[6 r 3] 7)45   [7] 8)56   [4 r 7] 9)43   [5] 6)30   [3 r 5] 10)35
[1 r 3] 9)12   [6 r 2] 5)32   [6 r 2] 7)44   [1 r 1] 7)8   [4 r 2] 8)34
[5 r 3] 10)53   [8 r 4] 9)76   [10 r 4] 5)54   [6 r 1] 7)43   [9] 3)27
[7] 6)42   [9] 7)63   [4 r 6] 9)42   [10 r 3] 8)83   [9 r 4] 5)49

Write the answer in the box.

8 ÷ 6 = [1 r 2]	12 ÷ 10 = [1 r 2]	11 ÷ 9 = [1 r 2]
13 ÷ 10 = [1 r 3]	17 ÷ 7 = [2 r 3]	23 ÷ 8 = [2 r 7]
70 ÷ 10 = [7]	70 ÷ 7 = [10]	54 ÷ 6 = [9]

As with the previous page, some of these problems work out exactly and others do not. Look out for the 3rd section where the numbers are small. Children sometimes lose track of 'which number is going into which' when both numbers are about the same size.

22 Choose the operation

Write either x or ÷ in the box.

6 [x] 7 = 42   24 [÷] 6 = 4   10 [÷] 2 = 5

Write either x or ÷ in the box.

35 [÷] 7 = 5	35 [÷] 5 = 7	7 [x] 5 = 35
5 [x] 7 = 35	6 [x] 9 = 54	54 [÷] 6 = 9
9 [x] 6 = 54	54 [÷] 9 = 6	32 [÷] 4 = 8
4 [x] 8 = 32	8 [x] 4 = 32	32 [÷] 8 = 4
4 [x] 9 = 36	36 [÷] 4 = 9	9 [x] 4 = 36
36 [÷] 9 = 4	80 [÷] 8 = 10	8 [x] 10 = 80
7 [x] 9 = 63	63 [÷] 7 = 9	63 [÷] 9 = 7
9 [x] 7 = 63	9 [x] 9 = 81	81 [÷] 9 = 9
64 [÷] 8 = 8	8 [x] 8 = 64	25 [÷] 5 = 5
5 [x] 5 = 25	16 [÷] 4 = 4	4 [x] 4 = 16
7 [x] 7 = 49	49 [÷] 7 = 7	3 [x] 3 = 9
9 [÷] 3 = 3	100 [÷] 10 = 10	10 [x] 10 = 100
50 [÷] 10 = 5	5 [x] 8 = 40	40 [÷] 4 = 10
20 [÷] 5 = 4	4 [x] 10 = 40	36 [÷] 6 = 6
3 [x] 7 = 21	21 [÷] 3 = 7	7 [x] 4 = 28
14 [x] 10 = 140	140 [÷] 2 = 70	70 [÷] 10 = 7
42 [÷] 6 = 7	7 [x] 10 = 70	72 [÷] 8 = 9
50 [÷] 5 = 10	20 [÷] 4 = 5	3 [x] 8 = 24

Much of this work is recalling times tables knowledge. See how quickly and comfortably children can move between multiplying and dividing.

23 Real life problems

Write the answer in the box.

There are 8 ink cartridges in each packet. How many cartridges will there be in 6 packets?   8 x 6 = 48   [48 cartridges]

Write the answer in the box.

Ian shares 50 oranges equally between 6 elephants and gives the remainder to the giraffes. How many oranges do the giraffes receive?   [8 r 2] 6)50   [2 oranges]

There are 9 children at a birthday party and each child has 4 chocolate cakes. How many chocolate cakes do the children have altogether?   9 x 4 = 36   [36 cakes]

Ben has 60 building bricks and puts them in piles of 7. How many piles of 7 can Ben make?   [8 r 4] 7)60   [8 piles]

Katy has seven 10p coins, four 5p coins, and two 2p coins. How much does she have altogether?   10 x 7 = 70 / 4 x 5 = 20 + / 2 x 2 = 4 / 94   [94p]

The dog buries four bones in each hole. The dog has 36 bones. How many holes must the dog dig?   [9] 4)36   [9 holes]

Questions 1 and 3 do not require answers in the usual form of 'x remainder y' and this may cause confusion. Children need to read the question carefully to find out exactly what is required. Hopefully, they should be able to answer the 4th problem in their heads`.

24 Perimeter

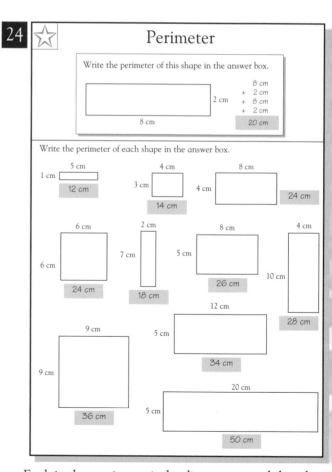

Write the perimeter of this shape in the answer box.

2 cm   8 cm
         + 2 cm
8 cm   + 8 cm
         + 2 cm
         [20 cm]

Write the perimeter of each shape in the answer box.

5 cm, 1 cm → [12 cm]
4 cm, 3 cm → [14 cm]
8 cm, 4 cm → [24 cm]
6 cm, 6 cm → [24 cm]
2 cm, 7 cm → [18 cm]
8 cm, 5 cm → [26 cm]
4 cm, 10 cm → [28 cm]
9 cm, 12 cm, 5 cm → [34 cm]
9 cm, 9 cm → [36 cm]
20 cm, 5 cm → [50 cm]

Explain that perimeter is the distance around the edge of a shape. There are a few methods used to find the perimeter of a square or rectangle: add two different sides together then double the number; double each side, then add them together; add each side one by one in sequence.

Area

Write the area of the shape in the answer box.

1 cm
7 cm

$1 \times 7 = 7$

7 cm²

Write the area of each shape in the answer box.

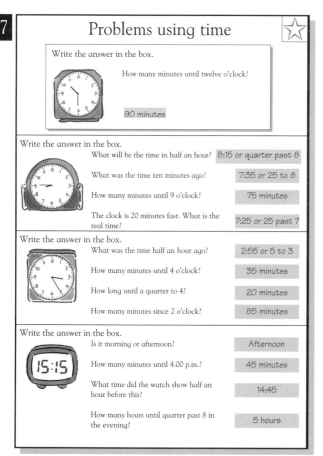

12 cm²

10 cm²

6 cm²

16 cm²

20 cm²

12 cm²

4 cm²

9 cm²

Since the area of a shape is the amount of space inside it, the number of squares inside each shape is the answer. Children should realise that multiplying one side by the other will give the same result more quickly. This does not work with shapes such as triangles.

Area

Write the area of this shape in the answer box.

3 cm
8 cm

$3 \times 8 = 24$

24 cm²

Write the area of each shape in the answer box.

9 cm
4 cm

36 cm²

10 cm
3 cm

30 cm²

3 cm
6 cm
12 cm

9 cm

54 cm²

9 cm
7 cm

63 cm²

36 cm²

7 cm
8 cm

10 cm

56 cm²

20 cm

200 cm²

25 cm
4 cm

100 cm²

Following on from the last page, this page requires children to find the areas by multiplying the sides together. If they are unsure, you could sketch in squares on the shapes to help.

Problems using time

Write the answer in the box.

How many minutes until twelve o'clock?

90 minutes

Write the answer in the box.

What will be the time in half an hour?	8:15 or quarter past 8
What was the time ten minutes ago?	7:35 or 25 to 8
How many minutes until 9 o'clock?	75 minutes
The clock is 20 minutes fast. What is the real time?	7:25 or 25 past 7

Write the answer in the box.

What was the time half an hour ago?	2:55 or 5 to 3
How many minutes until 4 o'clock?	35 minutes
How long until a quarter to 4?	20 minutes
How many minutes since 2 o'clock?	85 minutes

Write the answer in the box.

Is it morning or afternoon?	Afternoon
How many minutes until 4.00 p.m.?	45 minutes
What time did the watch show half an hour before this?	14:45
How many hours until quarter past 8 in the evening?	5 hours

Although children of this age can usually read and write the time from a clock, their deeper understanding is tested here. Problems are best dealt with by using a large kitchen clock. You can move hands around to illustrate questions.

Reading timetables

	Otterbourne	Compton	Badger Farm	Winchester
Redline Bus	8.00	8.05	8.15	8.25
Wincarry	8.05	No stop	8.12	8.20
Sean's taxi	8.30	8.35	8.45	8.55
Transtrax	8.07	No stop	No stop	8.15

The timetable shows the times it takes to travel using different transport companies between Otterbourne and Winchester.

Write the answer in the box.

How long does Redline take between Otterbourne and Winchester?

25 minutes

When does Wincarry arrive at Badger Farm?

8:12

Where does Transtrax not stop?

Compton and Badger farm

Where is Sean's taxi at 8.35?

Compton

Does Wincarry stop at Compton?

No

How long does Redline take to travel between Badger Farm and Winchester?

10 minutes

Which is the fastest trip between Otterbourne and Winchester?

Transtrax

Which service arrives at five minutes to nine?

Sean's taxi

How long does Sean's taxi take between Otterbourne and Badger Farm?

15 minutes

Where is Wincarry at twelve minutes past eight?

Badger farm

Reading timetables is an important skill and although children should find this exercise fairly straightforward, it is a good starting point to check that children are gaining information logically. Ask the children how they are finding the information.

Mode and median

Write the mode and the median of this row in the boxes.

| 4 | 2 | 2 | 1 | 6 | 3 | 2 |

The mode is **2**   The median is **2**

Write the mode of each row in the box.

2	3	7	4	2	7	2	1	**2**
7	4	1	4	8	5	3	4	**4**
5	3	5	3	5	3	4	5	**5**
7	5	9	7	2	4	8	6	**7**
4	3	4	3	4	3	4	5	**4**
0	4	2	7	3	8	2	9	**2**
3	2	1	2	2	3	2	3	**2**
8	3	6	3	8	2	8	4	**8**

Write the median of each row in the box.

4	8	6	3	9	6	7	**6**
5	9	2	6	9	1	4	**5**
6	3	8	6	1	7	6	**6**
3	8	6	7	5	9	4	**6**
1	8	3	4	2	6	5	**4**
9	5	8	6	4	7	9	**7**
2	5	2	3	1	2	3	**2**
6	3	7	4	5	8	6	**6**

Most teachers tell children to remember mode as 'most' and this helps in sorting out between median and mode. Median is the middle number if the numbers are in order, and in groups of 7 numbers it would be the 4th one.

Nets of 3D shapes

For which 3D shape is this the net?

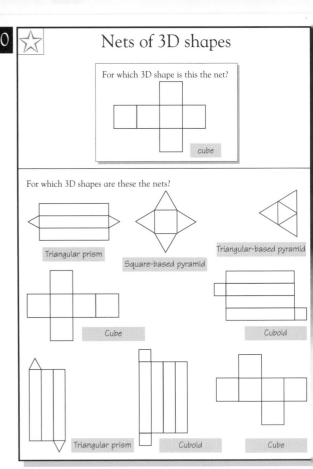

cube

For which 3D shapes are these the nets?

Triangular prism

Square-based pyramid

Triangular-based pyramid

Cube

Cuboid

Triangular prism

Cuboid

Cube

Most children are familiar with the shapes of nets although they can find it more difficult to draw the Some shapes, like the cube, have more than one n and it can be an interesting exercise to ask children find as many different nets for the cube as they can

Nets of 3D shapes

Draw a net for a cube.

Draw a net for these shapes.

Cuboid

Square-based pyramid

Cube (different to the example)

Triangular prism

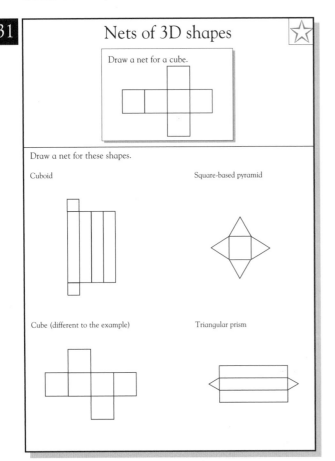

Each of these shapes has a number of different nets and it may be that the one the child has drawn is not the one shown. However, if in doubt, ask the children to cut out their net and see if it works. Complete this page without referring to the previous page!

Co-ordinates

Look at the grid and then answer the questions below.

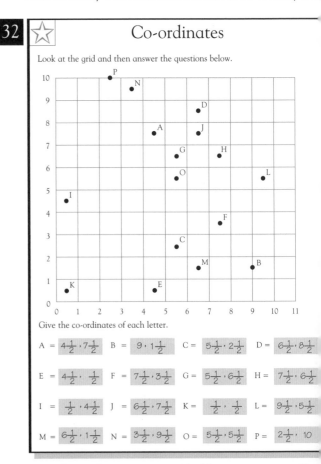

Give the co-ordinates of each letter.

A = $4\frac{1}{2}, 7\frac{1}{2}$ B = $9, 1\frac{1}{2}$ C = $5\frac{1}{2}, 2\frac{1}{2}$ D = $6\frac{1}{2}, 8\frac{1}{2}$

E = $4\frac{1}{2}, \frac{1}{2}$ F = $7\frac{1}{2}, 3\frac{1}{2}$ G = $5\frac{1}{2}, 6\frac{1}{2}$ H = $7\frac{1}{2}, 6\frac{1}{2}$

I = $\frac{1}{2}, 4\frac{1}{2}$ J = $6\frac{1}{2}, 7\frac{1}{2}$ K = $\frac{1}{2}, \frac{1}{2}$ L = $9\frac{1}{2}, 5\frac{1}{2}$

M = $6\frac{1}{2}, 1\frac{1}{2}$ N = $3\frac{1}{2}, 9\frac{1}{2}$ O = $5\frac{1}{2}, 5\frac{1}{2}$ P = $2\frac{1}{2}, 10$

Watch out for accuracy of half-squares especially when both co-ordinates involve halves. Check that the children always use the first co-ordinate as the across value and the second co-ordinate as the up value.

Real life problems

Work out the sum and then write the answer.

Tuhil is reading a book that
has 72 pages. He has read 38 pages.
How many more pages does
Tuhil have to read?

34 pages

$$\begin{array}{r} 72 \\ -38 \\ \hline 34 \end{array}$$

Work out the sum and then write the answer in the box.

Pat has 37 marbles and plays two
matches. He wins another 24 marbles
in the first match but then loses 18 in
the second match. How many
marbles does Pat have now?

Mary has 70 felt-tips but then gives
26 of them to Abir. She buys 12 new
felt-tips to replace the ones she has
given away. How many felt-tips does
Mary have now?

Billy empties his trouser pockets and
finds 26p in one pocket, 13p in
another pocket, and 37p in another
one. How much has Billy found
altogether?

Ann has 64 chips with her burger.
Ann eats 16 chips and gives 6 to her
baby brother. How many chips does
Ann have left?

Multiplying

Write the answer in the box

27 x 5	53 x 4	19 x 4
20 x 5 = 100	50 x 4 = 200	10 x 4 = 40
7 x 5 = 35	3 x 4 = 12	9 x 4 = 36
135	212	76

Write the answer between the lines.

26 x 4   43 x 4   67 x 4   18 x 4   74 x 4

19 x 3   41 x 3   58 x 3   32 x 3   94 x 3

33 x 5   49 x 5   67 x 5   28 x 5   63 x 5

64 x 2   85 x 2   94 x 2   57 x 2   78 x 2

15 x 6   53 x 6   64 x 6   85 x 6   72 x 6

37 x 8   85 x 8   51 x 8   84 x 8   47 x 8

Multiplying

Write the answer in the box

24 x 7	38 x 8	56 x 9
20 x 7 = 140	30 x 8 = 240	50 x 9 = 450
4 x 7 = 28	8 x 8 = 64	6 x 9 = 54
168	304	504

Write the answer between the lines.

43 x 7   50 x 7   37 x 7   29 x 7   16 x 7

27 x 9   58 x 9   36 x 9   14 x 9   61 x 9

53 x 10   37 x 10   49 x 10   58 x 10   67 x 10

37 x 4   47 x 5   87 x 6   17 x 7   97 x 8

58 x 6   38 x 7   78 x 8   28 x 9   18 x 10

49 x 5   29 x 6   59 x 7   89 x 8   69 x 9

Dividing

Write the answer in the box.

$24 \div 7 =$ ⬚ 3 r 3   ⬚ 4 r 1 $43 \div 8 =$ ⬚ 5 r 3

$5 \overline{)21}$

Write the answer in the box.

$27 \div 3 =$ ⬚	$14 \div 3 =$ ⬚	$23 \div 3 =$ ⬚
$7 \div 3 =$ ⬚	$31 \div 4 =$ ⬚	$14 \div 4 =$ ⬚
$38 \div 4 =$ ⬚	$4 \div 4 =$ ⬚	$42 \div 5 =$ ⬚
$23 \div 5 =$ ⬚	$15 \div 5 =$ ⬚	$27 \div 5 =$ ⬚
$47 \div 6 =$ ⬚	$35 \div 5 =$ ⬚	$46 \div 5 =$ ⬚
$24 \div 5 =$ ⬚	$42 \div 7 =$ ⬚	$60 \div 7 =$ ⬚

Write the answer in the box.

$8 \overline{)34}$ $8 \overline{)46}$ $8 \overline{)21}$ $8 \overline{)56}$ $9 \overline{)27}$

$9 \overline{)46}$ $9 \overline{)58}$ $9 \overline{)74}$ $2 \overline{)15}$ $2 \overline{)21}$

$2 \overline{)3}$ $2 \overline{)16}$ $3 \overline{)17}$ $3 \overline{)23}$ $3 \overline{)30}$

$3 \overline{)24}$ $4 \overline{)13}$ $4 \overline{)24}$ $4 \overline{)31}$ $4 \overline{)43}$

Write the answer in the box.

$45 \div 8 =$ ⬚	$73 \div 8 =$ ⬚	$56 \div 8 =$ ⬚
$73 \div 9 =$ ⬚	$41 \div 9 =$ ⬚	$50 \div 9 =$ ⬚
$54 \div 10 =$ ⬚	$89 \div 10 =$ ⬚	$42 \div 10 =$ ⬚

Dividing

Write the answer in the box.

31 ÷ 4 = [7 r 3]   [2 r 5]   31 ÷ 9 = [3 r 4]

6 ⟌ 17

Write the answer in the box.

46 ÷ 9 =   28 ÷ 7 =   45 ÷ 9 =

74 ÷ 8 =   32 ÷ 3 =   45 ÷ 7 =

61 ÷ 7 =   65 ÷ 9 =   12 ÷ 9 =

17 ÷ 4 =   24 ÷ 6 =   36 ÷ 6 =

37 ÷ 8 =   37 ÷ 9 =   37 ÷ 10 =

37 ÷ 6 =   54 ÷ 6 =   54 ÷ 7 =

Write the answer in the box.

7 ⟌ 45   8 ⟌ 56   9 ⟌ 43   6 ⟌ 30   10 ⟌ 35

9 ⟌ 12   5 ⟌ 32   7 ⟌ 44   7 ⟌ 8   8 ⟌ 34

10 ⟌ 53   9 ⟌ 76   5 ⟌ 54   7 ⟌ 43   3 ⟌ 27

6 ⟌ 42   7 ⟌ 63   9 ⟌ 42   8 ⟌ 83   5 ⟌ 49

Write the answer in the box.

8 ÷ 6 =   12 ÷ 10 =   11 ÷ 9 =

13 ÷ 10 =   17 ÷ 7 =   23 ÷ 8 =

70 ÷ 10 =   70 ÷ 7 =   54 ÷ 6 =

Choose the operation

Write either x or ÷ in the box.

6 [x] 7 = 42   24 [÷] 6 = 4   10 [÷] 2 = 5

Write either x or ÷ in the box.

35 [ ] 7 = 5   35 [ ] 5 = 7   7 [ ] 5 = 35

5 [ ] 7 = 35   6 [ ] 9 = 54   54 [ ] 6 = 9

9 [ ] 6 = 54   54 [ ] 9 = 6   32 [ ] 4 = 8

4 [ ] 8 = 32   8 [ ] 4 = 32   32 [ ] 8 = 4

4 [ ] 9 = 36   36 [ ] 4 = 9   9 [ ] 4 = 36

36 [ ] 9 = 4   80 [ ] 8 = 10   8 [ ] 10 = 80

7 [ ] 9 = 63   63 [ ] 7 = 9   63 [ ] 9 = 7

9 [ ] 7 = 63   9 [ ] 9 = 81   81 [ ] 9 = 9

64 [ ] 8 = 8   8 [ ] 8 = 64   25 [ ] 5 = 5

5 [ ] 5 = 25   16 [ ] 4 = 4   4 [ ] 4 = 16

7 [ ] 7 = 49   49 [ ] 7 = 7   3 [ ] 3 = 9

9 [ ] 3 = 3   100 [ ] 10 = 10   10 [÷] 10 = 100

50 [ ] 10 = 5   5 [ ] 8 = 40   40 [ ] 4 = 10

20 [ ] 5 = 4   4 [ ] 10 = 40   36 [ ] 6 = 6

3 [ ] 7 = 21   21 [ ] 3 = 7   7 [ ] 4 = 28

14 [ ] 10 = 140   140 [ ] 2 = 70   70 [ ] 10 = 7

42 [ ] 6 = 7   7 [ ] 10 = 70   72 [ ] 8 = 9

50 [ ] 5 = 10   20 [ ] 4 = 5   3 [ ] 8 = 24

Real life problems

Write the answer in the box.

There are 8 ink cartridges in each packet. How many cartridges will there be in 6 packets?

48 cartridges

$8 \times 6 = 48$

Write the answer in the box.

Ian shares 50 oranges equally between 6 elephants and gives the remainder to the giraffes. How many oranges do the giraffes receive?

There are 9 children at a birthday party and each child has 4 chocolate cakes. How many chocolate cakes do the children have altogether?

Ben has 60 building bricks and puts them in piles of 7. How many piles of 7 can Ben make?

Katy has seven 10p coins, four 5p coins, and two 2p coins. How much does she have altogether?

The dog buries four bones in each hole. The dog has 36 bones. How many holes must the dog dig?

Perimeter

Write the perimeter of this shape in the answer box.

2 cm

8 cm

	8 cm
+	2 cm
+	8 cm
+	2 cm
	20 cm

Write the perimeter of each shape in the answer box.

5 cm

1 cm

4 cm

3 cm

8 cm

4 cm

6 cm

6 cm

2 cm

7 cm

8 cm

5 cm

4 cm

10 cm

12 cm

5 cm

9 cm

9 cm

20 cm

5 cm

Area

Write the area of the shape in the answer box.

1 cm

7 cm

1 x 7 = 7

7 cm²

Write the area of each shape in the answer box.

Area

Write the area of this shape in the answer box.

3 cm

$3 \times 8 = 24$

8 cm

24 cm²

Write the area of each shape in the answer box.

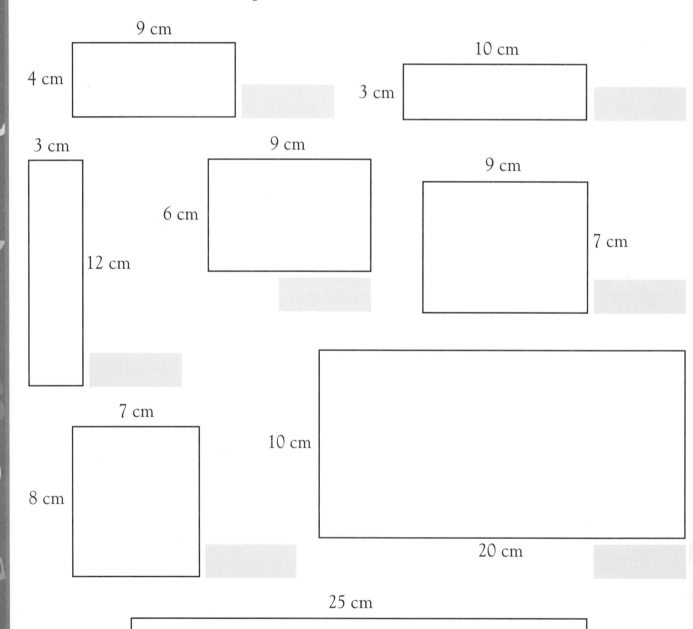

9 cm

4 cm

10 cm

3 cm

3 cm

9 cm

6 cm

12 cm

9 cm

7 cm

7 cm

10 cm

8 cm

20 cm

25 cm

4 cm

Problems using time

Write the answer in the box.

How many minutes until twelve o'clock?

90 minutes

quarter

Write the answer in the box.

7:45

quaurter to 8

What will be the time in half an hour?

quarter past 8
8:15

What was the time ten minutes ago?

25 to 8
7:35

How many minutes until 9 o'clock?

75 – 60+15

The clock is 20 minutes fast. What is the real time?

7:25

Write the answer in the box.

3:25

25 Past 3

What was the time half an hour ago? 2:00 3:25

2·55 5+03

How many minutes until 4 o'clock?

35 mins

How long until a quarter to 4?

20 mins

How many minutes since 2 o'clock?

1 hr 25 mins

Write the answer in the box.

3·15 pm

20:15

3:25
8:15

Is it morning or afternoon?

afternoon

How many minutes until 4.00 p.m.?

45 mins

What time did the watch show half an hour before this?

14:45

How many hours until quarter past 8 in the evening?

5 hours

Reading timetables

	Otterbourne	Compton	Badger Farm	Winchester
Redline Bus	8.00	8.05	8.15	8.25
Wincarry	8.05	No stop	8.12	8.20
Sean's taxi	8.30	8.35	8.45	8.55
Transtrax	8.07	No stop	No stop	8.15

The timetable shows the times it takes to travel using different transport companies between Otterbourne and Winchester.

Write the answer in the box.

How long does Redline take between Otterbourne and Winchester?

When does Wincarry arrive at Badger Farm?

Where does Transtrax not stop?

Where is Sean's taxi at 8.35?

Does Wincarry stop at Compton?

How long does Redline take to travel between Badger Farm and Winchester?

Which is the fastest trip between Otterbourne and Winchester?

Which service arrives at five minutes to nine?

How long does Sean's taxi take between Otterbourne and Badger Farm?

Where is Wincarry at twelve minutes past eight?

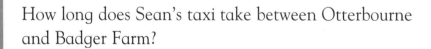

Mode and median

Write the mode and the median of this row in the boxes.

4	2	2	1	6	3	2

The mode is 2   The median is 2

Write the mode of each row in the box.

2	3	7	4	2	7	2	1	
7	4	1	4	8	5	3	4	
5	3	5	3	5	3	4	5	
7	5	9	7	2	4	8	6	
4	3	4	3	4	3	4	5	
0	4	2	7	3	8	2	9	
3	2	1	2	2	3	2	3	
8	3	6	3	8	2	8	4	

Write the median of each row in the box.

4	8	6	3	9	6	7	
5	9	2	6	9	1	4	
6	3	8	6	1	7	6	
3	8	6	7	5	9	4	
1	8	3	4	2	6	5	
9	5	8	6	4	7	9	
2	5	2	3	1	2	3	
6	3	7	4	5	8	6	

Nets of 3D shapes

For which 3D shape is this the net?

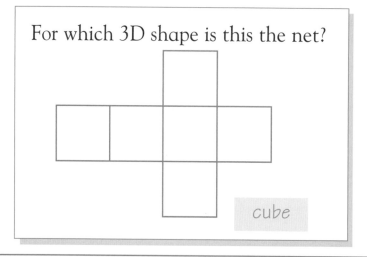

cube

For which 3D shapes are these the nets?

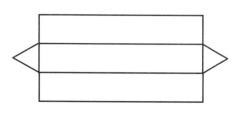

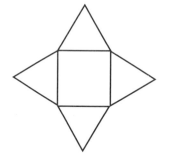

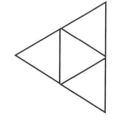

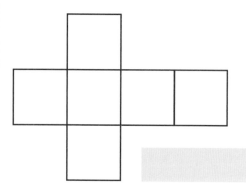

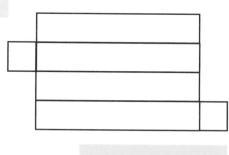

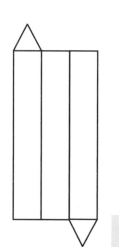

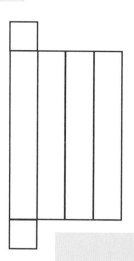

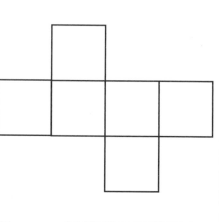

Nets of 3D shapes

Draw a net for a cube.

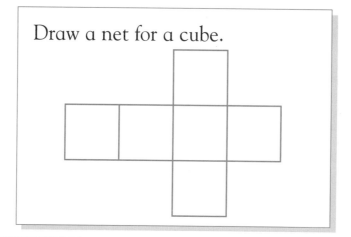

Draw a net for these shapes.

Cuboid

Square-based pyramid

Cube (different to the example)

Triangular prism

Co-ordinates

Look at the grid and then answer the questions below.

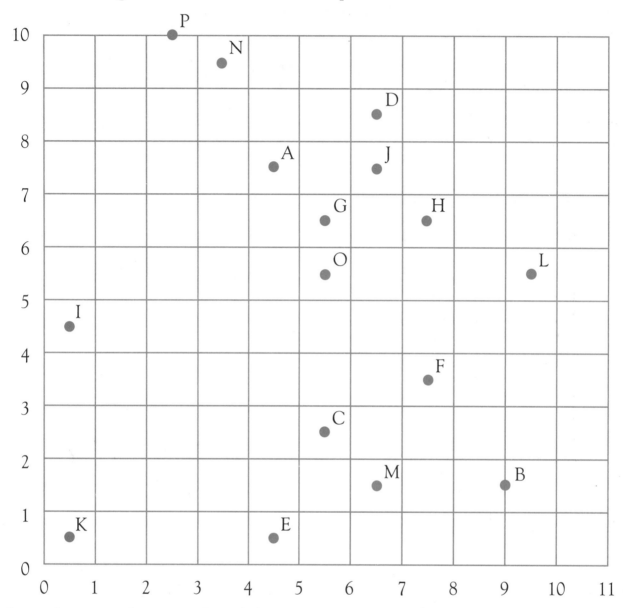

Give the co-ordinates of each letter.

A = $4\frac{1}{2}$, $7\frac{1}{2}$ B =   C =   D =

E =   F =   G =   H =

I =   J =   K =   L =

M =   N =   O =   P =